D1452816

Short Vowel Phonics 1: short a, i, o, u, e

by: Patricia J. Norton

illustrated by: Sarah E. Cashman

Other reading material by the Author:

Short Vowel Phonics 2
Short Vowel Phonics 3
Short Vowel Phonics 4
Short Vowel Phonics Short Stories
Decodable Alphabet Chart

ISBN 978-0-9817710-0-7 (lib. bdg.)
[1. Reading - Phonetic method. 2. Reading readiness. 3. Phonics]

shortvowelphonics.com

Printed and Bound in United States of America

Text font: Pen Time Manuscript

Table of Contents

A Cat, a Cap

Note to parents and teachers: Please have the child read the title before beginning the story. The title of the story, the pictures and the text are coordinated in such a way that a child will have read the word once before they are shown a picture of the word. This is to insure the child is learning to decode the word and not just guess.

Jan had a cap.

The cat ran at the cap.

The cat taps the cap.

The cat can jab the cap.

Jab! Jab!

The cap has a gap.

Is the cat a bad cat?

Sam and the Hat

Sam had a hat.

A cat ran at the hat.

The cat sat.

The hat sags.

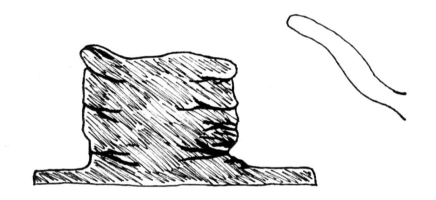

The cat ran.

Sam taps at the hat.

Sam taps and taps and taps.

Sam has a hat.

Vic's Rig

Vic had a big rig.

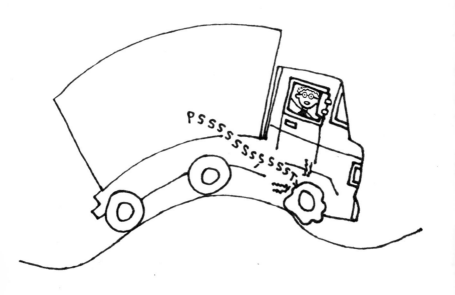

The rig hit a big pin.

It quit.

Vic did fix the big rig.

A Zig-Zag Rip

Mim has a sib.

Liz is Mim's sib.

Mim had a bib.

The bib did rip.

It had a zig-zag rip.

Liz did fix the rip.

A Dog, a Cot

Dot is Ron's dog.

Dot had hot dogs and
bon-bons.

And Dot had bon-bons and
hot dogs.

Dot sobs.

Ron got Dot a cot.

30

The Pom-pom

Mom has Tod.

Tod is Mom's tot.

Tod has a pom-pom.

Tod lobs the pom-pom

on the cot.

Mom lobs the pom-pom
on the box.

Tod has the pom-pom and the box.

The Sub

Gus has a sub.

The sub runs.

The sub runs up.

Gus: "The sub is fun."

Rub the Tug

Gus has a dud tug in a tub.

Gus rubs the tug.

The tug hums.

The tug runs and runs.

The tug runs in the tub.

Wet Jets

Ted is ten.

Ted met Lek.

Lek is ten.

Lek has a jet.

Ted has a red jet.

Ted and Lek

get the jets wet.

A Jet

Bev and Ben had a jet.

The jet gets wet.

Can the jet rev up?

Yes! Yes!

The jet can rev up.

The end